*Adore*naments™
Activity Book

Creative Reproducible Pages and Craft Ideas for Children
Honoring the Names of Christ

©Copyright 1998
Published by FamilyLife

FamilyLife is a division of Campus Crusade for Christ, Inc., an evangelical Christian organization founded in 1951 by Bill Bright. Dennis Rainey, executive director of FamilyLife, helped begin this ministry to families in 1976. FamilyLife strengthens marriages and homes and then equips them to go to the world with the gospel of Jesus Christ. FamilyLife Conferences are held in many cities throughout the United States. Information on FamilyLife resources may be obtained by writing or calling FamilyLife at the address and telephone numbers listed below.

Most Scriptures are quoted from the *New American Standard Bible.* Copyright © 1960, 1962, 1963, 1971, 1972, 1973, 1975, 1977 by the Lockman Foundation. Used by permission.

Other Scripture quotations are from:
The Living Bible (TLB) © 1971. Used by permission of Tyndale House Publishers, Inc., Wheaton, IL 60187.

New International Version®. NIV®. Copyright © 1973, 1978, 1984 by International Bible Society. Used by permission of Zondervan Publishing House. All rights reserved.

Printed in the United States of America
ISBN 1-57229-116-8

Contributors: Ben Colter, Diane Jonasson, Mary Larmoyeux, Lee Smith, and Mark Whitlock

A special thanks to Linda Shepherd who prompted us to create this resource.

FAMILYLIFE™
Bringing Timeless Principles Home

P.O. Box 23840
Little Rock, AR 72221-3840
1-800-FL-TODAY
http://www.familylife-ccc.org

*A*dorenaments™
Activity Book

Creative Reproducible Pages and Craft Ideas for Children
Honoring the Names of Christ

When Jesus Christ came into the world, He was born in a simple stable, one filled with the unmistakable sounds and smells of oxen and sheep. As Scripture tells us in Luke 2:7, our Redeemer was "laid in a manger, because there was no room for [Him] in the inn." Imagine that—no room for the Savior of the world.

Through FamilyLife's Adorenaments™ (a collection of 12 colorful ornaments—each revealing a name of Christ), its companion storybook, *What Nick and Holly Found in Grandpa's Attic,* and now this *Adorenaments Activity Book,* you can make room for Jesus this Christmas. Help the children you love:

★ Construct and color their own set of Adorenaments
★ Prepare a special booklet that recalls and explains the names of Jesus Christ
★ Creatively interact with the biblical names of Jesus through crafts

Choose and adapt the ideas for the special children in your Sunday school group, classroom, neighborhood, or home. These hands-on projects will help the boys and girls grasp the various names of our Savior that are presented by FamilyLife's Adorenaments—Immanuel, the Door, the True Vine, and others.

You may want to complete your special Christmas activities with a holiday "goody bag" for the children. It could include: their completed booklet and set of ornaments, a coloring book about the first Christmas, a candy cane, one of the actual FamilyLife Adorenaments, a pocket-size New Testament, an age appropriate storybook about Jesus' life, or a picture of the child (or class) making Adorenaments.

Just have fun and measure your success by the smiles on the children's faces and the newly discovered truths about Jesus in their hearts.

Make Your Own Adorenaments™

Note to Parent or Teacher: The boys and girls will color ornaments in this section that depict specific names of Jesus. Consider duplicating the ornaments onto card stock or special paper, cutting them out, and laminating the finished product. By punching holes and attaching yarn or ribbon, the children will have personal sets of Adorenaments that can be treasured for years to come.

Immanuel

True Vine

The Door

Giver of Living Water

Light of the World

Lion from the tribe of Judah

Bright Morning Star

Lamb of God

Good Shepherd

Bread of Life

King of kings and Lord of lords

Savior

Instructions:

Have fun making your own special booklet about the names of Jesus.

- ☆ First, cut out each page along the solid lines.
- ☆ Next, fold on the dotted horizontal line and then on the dotted vertical line in order to create the booklet pages.
- ☆ Assemble the cover and pages in order from one through twelve by fitting them inside each other. Staple along the center fold.

Share your booklet with your family and friends and discover the real meaning of Christmas together.

Adorenaments™

My Book About Jesus

Name _____

Jesus is the Bread of Life

Homemade bread smells great, but I have to taste it to know for sure. When Jesus is my Savior, He is my Bread of Life.

Jesus replied, "I am the Bread of Life. No one coming to me will ever be hungry again."

—John 6:35a (TLB)

Jesus is the Door

Just as I enter my home through a door, I can enter heaven only through Jesus.

"I am the door; if anyone enters through Me, he shall be saved..."

—John 10:9

Jesus is the Savior

Jesus wants to be my Savior, but I must ask Him into my heart.

...and now tell all the world that God sent his Son to be their Savior.
—1 John 4:14 (TLB)

Jesus is Immanuel

Jesus came as "God with us" to show me what God is like.

"...and they will call him Immanuel"—which means, "God with us."

—Matthew 1:23
(New International Version)

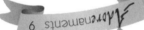

Jesus is the Good Shepherd

Sometimes I don't know what to do. I can always turn to Jesus who will lead me in the right direction—just like a shepherd leads his sheep.

"I am the good shepherd; the good shepherd lays down His life for the sheep."
—John 10:11

Adorenaments 9

Jesus is the Giver of Living Water

When I am thirsty, a cool drink of water tastes so good! When Jesus becomes my Savior, He gives me the Holy Spirit who fills my soul with His goodness.

He replied, "If you only knew…you would ask me for some living water!"
—John 4:10 (TLB)

Adorenaments 4

Adorenaments 10

Jesus is the King of kings and Lord of lords

Jesus is more powerful than earthly kings. They will all bow down to Jesus one day as the Lord of lords.

He…is the King of kings and Lord of lords.

—1 Timothy 6:15b

Adorenaments 3

Jesus is the True Vine

When a branch falls off of a grapevine, it cannot make new grapes. Jesus is the True Vine. It is important for me to stay joined to Him by obeying His Word and praying.

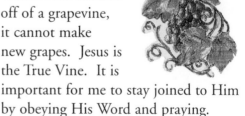

"Yes, I am the Vine; you are the branches…apart from me you can't do a thing."

Jesus is the Lion from the tribe of Judah

Lions are strong and powerful. Jesus is the strongest of all. When I think of how small I am, and who Jesus is, I feel very safe.

"...behold, the Lion that is from the tribe of Judah..."
—Revelation 5:5

Jesus is the Bright Morning Star

Bright stars fill the night sky with their light and make me feel happy. Jesus is happy when I bring His light to my family and friends.

"...I am...the bright Morning Star."
—Revelation 22:16

Jesus is the Lamb of God

Jesus was sent to earth by His Father and He paid for the world's sins by dying on the cross. He wants to be my Savior.

"...Look! There is the Lamb of God who takes away the world's sin!"
—John 1:29 (TLB)

Jesus is the Light of the World

If my room is dark and I start to fall over a toy, I turn on a light. Then I am no longer afraid of tripping, because I can see. Jesus helps me see every day when I let Him guide me with His light.

..."I am the Light of the world. So if you follow me, you won't be stumbling through the darkness, for living light will flood your path."
—John 8:12 (TLB)

Christmas Crafts with Adorenaments™

Note to Parent or Teacher: These crafts will encourage interaction about the names of Jesus. It will be helpful if you show the boys and girls a finished craft when you are giving them instructions. You will want to adapt ideas according to the children's ages and skill-levels. The *Adorenaments Activity Book* is designed for use with FamilyLife's Adorenaments and its companion storybook, *What Nick and Holly Found in Grandpa's Attic.*

Manger

Name of Jesus: *Immanuel*
Reference: Matthew 1:23

Objective: To remind the children of *Immanuel*—God with us. The boys and girls will make a small manger that they can place in their homes.

Materials:
- ☆ Four craft sticks per child (You could also use Popsicle sticks or clothespins. If you use clothespins, take them apart for this craft.)
- ☆ Craft glue
- ☆ Card stock (could use cardboard, file folders, or heavy construction paper)
- ☆ Pine straw (could substitute hay or shredded paper)

Approximate teacher preparation time: 3 minutes per manger
- ☆ To form the ends of the manger, make an "x" by gluing two sticks together. (Each child will need two upright x's.)
- ☆ Cut rectangles of card stock (one per child—approximately 2 1/2" by 3"); older children could cut the rectangles themselves.

Approximate time for craft: 10-20 minutes

Actual craft: Manger

Instructions: (While the children are waiting for their mangers to dry, refer to FamilyLife's Adorenaments or read the storybook *What Nick and Holly Found in Grandpa's Attic.*)

1. Each child should receive two x's (prepared in advance).
2. Fold a pre-cut rectangle in half lengthwise and glue it between the two x's to form the bed of the manger. (Older children will cut the rectangles themselves.)
3. Allow manger to dry.
4. Glue pine straw (hay or shredded paper) onto the bed of the manger.

Door Banner

Name of Jesus: *The Door*
Reference: John 10:9

Objective: To remind the children that Jesus is *the Door* to eternal life as they prepare banners to be hung over a door. Whoever comes to the door will read the words of John 14:6, "I am the way, the truth, and the life. No one comes to the Father except through me."

Materials:
- ☆ Butcher paper (could use shelf paper)—enough for one 2-3 foot long banner per child
- ☆ Paints and paintbrushes (could use crayons or markers)
- ☆ Old shirts or smocks to protect children's clothing

Approximate teacher preparation time: 2 minutes per banner for young children; older children could do the entire craft themselves.
- ☆ Cut butcher paper into lengths that are 2-3 feet.
- ☆ Print the following on banners for younger children: "I am the way, the truth, and the life. No one comes to the Father except through me." John 14:6 (Older children can do the printing themselves.)

Approximate time for craft: 10-20 minutes

Actual craft: Door banner

Instructions:
1. Children will print "Our Christmas message to you" on butcher paper followed by the words of John 14:6.
2. Children will decorate their banners with paints, markers, crayons, etc.

The True Vine

Name of Jesus: *The True Vine*
Reference: John 15:5

Objective: To remind the children that Jesus is ***the True Vine***, and that we must stay connected to Him by obeying His Word and praying.

Materials:
- ☆ Sticks from a tree (at least one per child)
- ☆ Green pipe cleaners
- ☆ Large purple craft beads (be sure the pipe cleaner will fit through the hole in beads)
- ☆ Glue
- ☆ Silk or paper grape leaves

Approximate teacher preparation time: None-10 minutes
- ☆ Older children can do this entire project themselves.
- ☆ For children under 5 years of age: Thread some craft beads onto green pipe cleaners and follow steps 1-5 below.

Approximate time for craft: 10 minutes

Actual craft: Grapes on a vine

Instructions: (**Note:** Young children will follow only steps 6 and 7.)
1. Thread a large plastic craft bead to the middle of a green pipe cleaner.
2. Take both ends of the pipe cleaner and give a one-turn twist (as you would a garbage bag twist tie).
3. Add a new bead to each end and give each a one-turn twist as you did in step two.
4. Continue adding beads (and twisting pipe cleaner) until there is 1/2 inch left on each end of the pipe cleaner.
5. The beads should begin to look like a bunch of grapes.
6. Twist the open ends together one turn and then attach to the tree stick making a hook shape and twisting the pipe cleaner around the stick.
7. Repeat steps 1-6 as needed, gluing or wrapping silk or paper grape leaves as desired.

Water Jug

Objective: To remind the children that Jesus is **the Giver of the Holy Spirit**, Living Water. With Him, our spiritual thirst is satisfied.

Materials:
- ☆ 1 empty plastic gallon milk jug per child
- ☆ Blue tissue paper
- ☆ Glue
- ☆ Scissors

Approximate teacher preparation time: 1 minute per jug (for children under 5 years of age)
- ☆ Older children can do the entire craft themselves.
- ☆ Cut the top of the plastic milk carton off for young children (above the handle).

Approximate time for craft: 5-10 minutes

Actual craft: Water jug

Instructions:
1. Using scissors, older children will cut off the top of plastic gallon milk containers (above the handle).
2. Younger children will be given pre-cut containers.
3. Children will glue strips of blue tissue paper onto outside of jug to make imaginary water.
4. You may want to have the children reenact the story in John 4 with their jugs.

Candle

Name of Jesus: *The Light of the World*
Reference: John 8:12

Objective: To remind the children that Jesus is able to bring light to anyone's life, no matter how dark or bad it may be. He is *the Light of the World.*

Materials:
- ☆ 1 Empty toilet tissue roll per child
- ☆ Aluminum foil or flame-colored plastic wrap
- ☆ Tissue paper
- ☆ 1 Dessert-size paper plate per child, preferably with a Christmas design
- ☆ Glue sticks
- ☆ Craft glue
- ☆ Poster board
- ☆ One box of Kleenex
- ☆ Copies of Bible verse (to glue onto candle)

Approximate teacher preparation time: 5-10 minutes per candle
- ☆ Cut the tissue paper the width of the toilet tissue tube so that it wraps around the tube and overlaps by one inch. Cut the length of the tissue paper one inch longer on each end to allow ample room for little fingers to tuck in the ends. (This should be 2 inches longer than the actual length of the tube.)
- ☆ Using the pattern below, cut flame shapes from poster board and cover in aluminum foil/plastic wrap. Older children will do this themselves.
- ☆ Have a copy of John 8:12 for each child.
- ☆ Place one tissue roll, 1 Kleenex, one piece of tissue paper cut to size, one printed Bible verse, and a glue stick at each place.

Approximate time for craft: 20 minutes

Actual Craft: Candle

Instructions:
1. Have each child place a line of glue down the length of the toilet tissue tube.

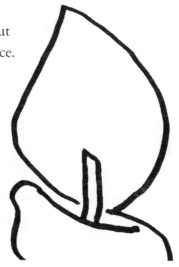

2. Set the tube in the center of the tissue paper square and tightly roll the paper around the tube until it overlaps.
3. Use the glue stick to secure the overlapping ends.
4. Carefully tuck in both ends of the tube by gently folding them into the tube.
5. Place a drop of craft glue around the bottom end of the tube and press it into the center of the dessert plate.
6. Wad the Kleenex into a medium-size ball.
7. Open a fold in the center of the Kleenex ball and slide the "flame" (poster board covered with either aluminum foil or flame colored plastic wrap) into the fold.
8. Carefully stuff the Kleenex into the top of the tube. A few drops of glue may be used to secure it in place.
9. Glue the Bible verse onto the candle as a reminder that Jesus is the Light of the World.

Star

Name of Jesus: *The Bright Morning Star*
Reference: Revelation 22:16

Objective: To remind the children that Jesus is ***the Bright Morning Star***. The Bible uses the word "star" to describe a prince or ruler. Jesus is the Prince of Peace and the giver of all true light. If we follow Him, He will cause His light to shine in our lives.

Materials:
- ☆ Cardboard, poster board, or foam core board
- ☆ Aluminum foil
- ☆ Glitter and glue (optional)
- ☆ Scissors
- ☆ String, yarn, or ribbon

Approximate teacher preparation time: 1 minute per star
(for children under 5 years of age)
- ☆ Enlarge pattern at right (on a copier) or make your own.
- ☆ Cut stars for younger children.
- ☆ Cut several star patterns for older children.

Approximate time for craft: 5-10 minutes

Actual craft: Star

Instructions:
1. Younger children will cover pre-cut stars with aluminum foil.
2. Older children will cut their own stars (using patterns) and will cover them with aluminum foil.
3. If you desire, the children can add glitter to their stars.
4. Poke a hole in the top of the star and attach a string/ribbon for hanging.

Lion

Name of Jesus: *The Lion From the Tribe of Judah*
Reference: Revelation 5:5

Objective: To remind the children that Jesus is **the Lion from the tribe of Judah.** A lion's gold coat and long, thick mane make him look like he is the king of all animals. He is also the largest of all cats. The tribe of Judah is a special group, or royal tribe of God's people, the Jews. So, Jesus is the Lion from the tribe of Judah.

Materials:
☆ Gold card stock or construction paper
☆ Gold yarn
☆ Glue

Approximate teacher preparation time: 3 minutes per lion
☆ Enlarge and duplicate (on a copier) the picture of the lion to the right onto card stock or construction paper.
☆ Cut yarn into 3 inch lengths.

Approximate time for craft: 10 minutes

Actual craft: Lion

Instructions:

1. The children will fold the lengths of yarn in half and will glue them onto the picture of the lion to make his mane.

2. They will print the words of Revelation 5:5 below the picture of the lion.

Lamb

Name of Jesus: *The Lamb of God*
Reference: John 1:29

Objective: To remind the children that Jesus is **the Lamb of God** who willingly obeyed His Father, went to the cross, and died for sinners. We are all sinners.

Materials:

- ☆ An adult-size white sock
- ☆ Wobble eyes (2 for each child)
- ☆ White pom poms or cotton balls (at least five for each child)
- ☆ Black pom pom for nose (or black felt)
- ☆ Washable pink felt for tongue
- ☆ Washable black felt for ears
- ☆ Washable fabric glue (can be found in craft stores)

Approximate teacher preparation time: 5 minutes per lamb

- ☆ Pre-cut felt for the tongues and ears.

Approximate time for craft: 15-20 minutes

Actual craft: Lamb (See diagram at right)

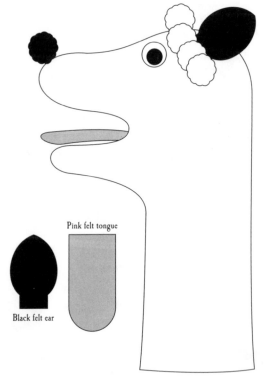

Pink felt tongue

Black felt ear

Instructions:

1. Use heel of the sock for the head and toe of the sock for the nose.
2. Children should glue ears to the side of the heel so that the ears stick up (see diagram).
3. Glue eyes in front of ears.
4. For mouth—stick hand into sock and tuck toe end of it into your hand (shaping it into a "C." Insert the flat edge of the tongue into the "C" and glue it to the sock).
5. Glue black pom pom for nose and white pom poms for lamb's wool.

Shepherd's Staff

Name of Jesus: *The Good Shepherd*
Reference: John 10:11

Objective: To remind the children that Jesus is *the Good Shepherd* who willingly laid down His life for His people—the sheep of His hand.

Materials:
- ☆ Three *long* brown pipe cleaners

Approximate teacher preparation time: None

Approximate time for craft: 5 minutes

Actual craft: Shepherd's staff

Instructions:

1. Have the children braid three long brown pipe cleaners together.
2. Round off the edges and bend to form a shepherd's staff.

Crown

Name of Jesus: *The King of Kings and Lord of Lords*
Reference: 1 Timothy 6:15

Objective: To remind the children that Jesus is **the King of kings and Lord of lords** and rules over all kings and rulers of the earth.

Materials:
- ☆ Yellow poster board
- ☆ Markers
- ☆ *Optional:* glitter, craft store gems, macaroni, or colored cereal shapes (Consider the children's ages. Avoid small objects for young children.)
- ☆ Scissors

Approximate teacher preparation time: 5-15 minutes
- ☆ Enlarge pattern on next page (on a copier) or make your own.
- ☆ Cut crowns for younger children from yellow poster board.
- ☆ Cut several crown patterns for older children.
- ☆ Cut rectangular strips to form headbands.

Approximate time for craft: 10-15 minutes (depending on how ornately decorated)

Actual craft: Crown

Instructions:
1. Older children will cut crown from yellow poster board using the patterns you have available, and then decorate them.
2. Younger children will decorate pre-cut crowns with markers, glitter, etc.
3. Glue or tape the strip to the back of the crown to form a headband. (Consider the size that each child will need.)
4. To finish the crown, either (1) Join the ends of the strip together by using tape or glue, or (2) Make adjustable slits.

Yellow poster board strip with slits

Bread

Name of Jesus: *The Bread of Life*
Reference: John 6:35

Objective: To remind the children that Jesus is *the Bread of Life*. He is the spiritual bread that we all need.

Materials:

☆ Frozen rolls, loaves of bread (or heat and serve)
☆ Paper plates or napkins

Approximate teacher preparation time: 5 minutes

☆ Follow thawing directions on the packages of frozen rolls or bread prior to baking.

Approximate time for craft: Refer to package directions for baking time.

Actual craft: Bread

Instructions:

1. Let the children watch you put the bread into the oven. Allow them to enjoy the smell of baking bread and watch it rise. While it is baking, refer to FamilyLife's Adorenaments or read the storybook *What Nick and Holly Found in Grandpa's Attic.*
2. Discuss how we should long for fellowship with Jesus, who is the Bread of Life, just as we long for fresh bread when we smell it cooking.
3. Allow the children to eat the freshly baked bread and discuss John 6:35.

Cross

Name of Jesus: *The Savior*
Reference: 1 John 4:14-15

Objective: To remind the children that Jesus is ***the Savior*** whose death on the cross for sin provided the only way we can have a relationship with God. The children will make puzzles out of crosses. The teacher will give examples of sin to the children, and this will be followed by a time of prayer and reflection. The children will then write some of their sins on the crosses before cutting them into puzzles. Afterwards, they will discuss how Jesus' death on the cross totally paid for the believers' sins and how He puts our lives together.

Materials:

☆ Heavy-weight, light-brown construction paper (or cardboard)
☆ Plastic laminating (can usually be found in grocery stores near the shelf paper or in office supply stores)
☆ Scissors
☆ Fine-tip markers

Approximate teacher preparation time: 5 minutes

☆ Prepare several crosses that the children can use as patterns (at least 5″ in length).

Approximate time for craft: 15 minutes

Actual craft: Cross Puzzle

Instructions:

1. Children will trace cross patterns and cut individual crosses.
2. Older children will write some of their sins on the crosses. (You can help younger children with this.)
3. The crosses will be covered with laminating material.
4. They will then be cut into several pieces to form a puzzle.
5. Discuss how our lives can be whole and complete when we put our faith in Jesus Christ and believe that He died on the cross for our sins.
6. Have the children put their cross puzzles together and recite 1 John 4:14-15.